DATE DUE		

WHEEL
on the
CHIMNEY

by Margaret Wise Brown and
Tibor Gergely

PHILADELPHIA   J. B. LIPPINCOTT COMPANY   NEW YORK

First there was one stork,

Then there were two.

They had just arrived from Africa.

They built a nest on a wheel on top of
a chimney.

They built in the spring when there was
no smoke and the chimney would
not be used again until winter.

First there was one stork, then there were two, soon there were four—the mother and father stork and two hungry babies with wide open beaks and white feathers.

The mother kept the little storks safe and warm under her wings while the father went out to get food for them.

Sometimes the father would keep them warm while the mother went fishing in the cool green rivers of Hungary.

Summer followed spring, cool and green. And the young storks grew longer legs. Their bills grew longer, but they never made a sound, for a stork is a silent bird.

The only sound he makes is the great clap-clapping of his beak.

In the olden days storks built nests on trees.

But it is considered a great honor to have a stork settle on your house— great honor and great good luck.

Some farmers bind cartwheels to the tops of their chimneys, or make platforms of twigs and straw, to invite the storks to land.

And while the other birds sing and the barnyard fowl cackle and crow and quack and hiss and cluck all through the long green summer, the storks are silent—silent and beautiful.

Then one day the air grew colder, and
a black stork arrived from the wild
forests to the North.
More and more storks, wild black ones
and great white ones that built
their nest on wheels on the chimneys of houses, flew down from the
sky and into a great green field.

The time to go South had come.

The storks would all fly South for the
winter.

How did they know, who had lived all
summer on the wheel on the chimney?

Then silently in great white flight they
flew over the towns of Europe.

Over rivers and bridges and far away,
always to the South.

They flew to the edge of the blue Mediterranean Sea and headed across the sea to Africa.

To the land of the Nile, where their cousins, great flocks of crimson flamingos the color of sunset, waded knee deep in the green waters of the river.

But they did not stop here–they flew on, high in the air to the South.

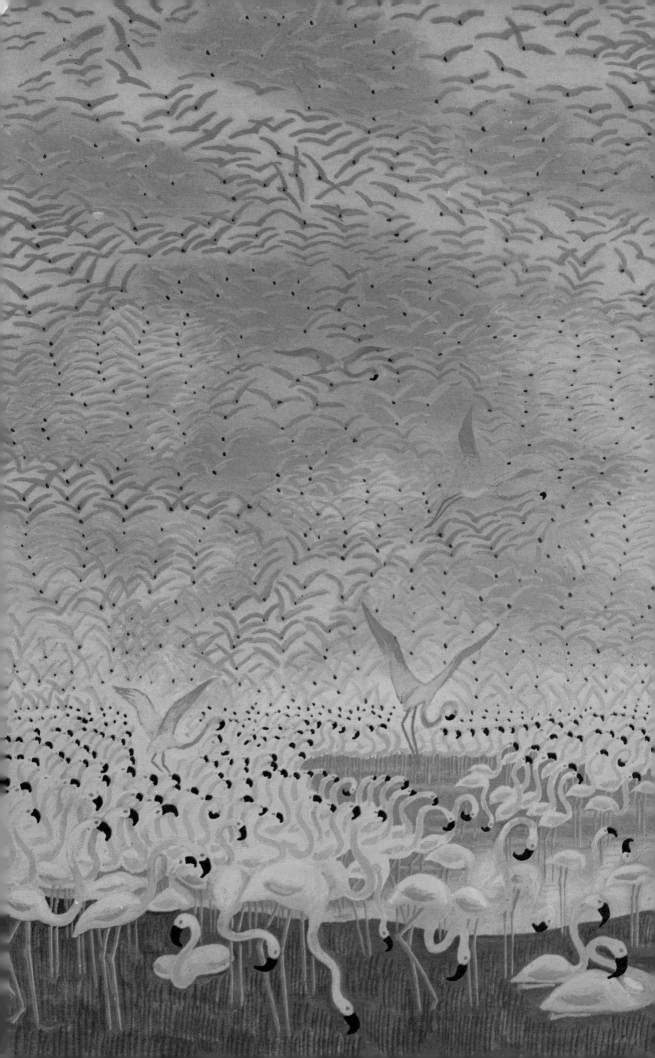

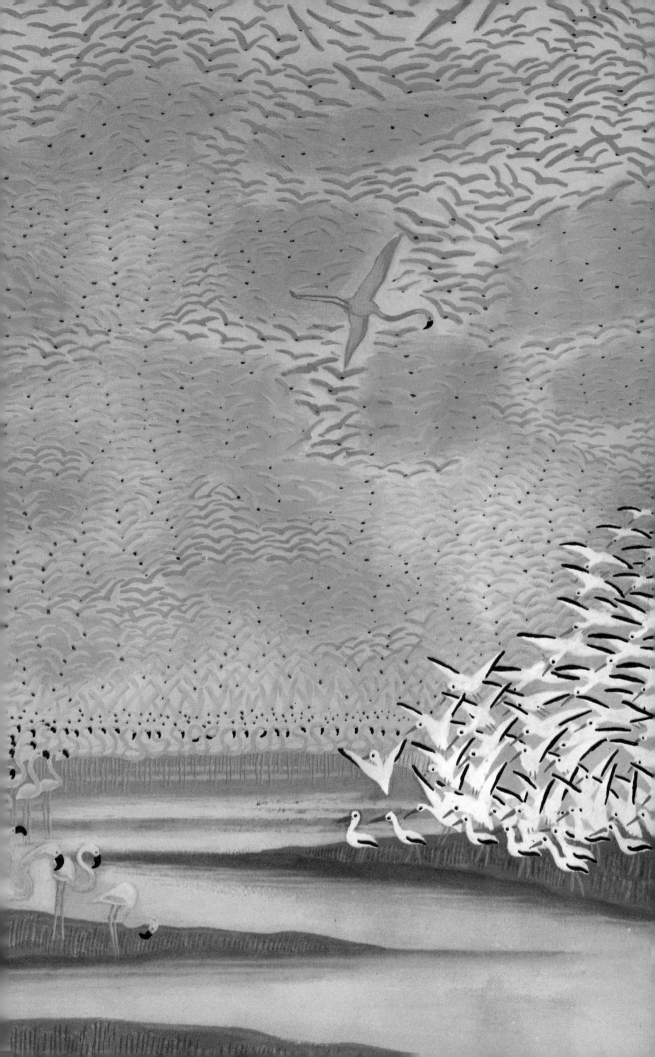

And here they lived for the winter – deep in the warm wild wilderness of Africa. And here where it was warm, they would stay until spring. And then one day great flocks of storks would gather and it would be time for the great flight to the North.

How did they know in that far away
   land that spring had come in the
   lands of the North?
This is still a secret of the storks—North
   or South.

The wild black storks would fly with the white storks, though the black storks would fly further to the North than the white storks—into the great green forests—far from the farms of men where the white stork made his home.

Off they started up through the air to the North.

But a great storm shook the sky.

Golden lightning split the air and the storks were blown far out over the Indian Ocean, far off their course and away from the lands to the North.

One white stork was very tired. He was too tired.

So he collapsed
onto the deck of
a boat bound for
Egypt.

When the captain saw that a weary
stork had landed on his ship, he
knew good luck had come his way.

He gave the stork a great wicker chair
like a nest to rest in. And he sent
him French croissants and yellow
tomatoes and good things to eat.
And the captain grew fond of the stork.
One day the stork flew away and the
captain wished him a safe journey.

Over the jungles where the monkeys chattered and the baboons squealed, mid the shrill screech of the wild parrot and the pink cockatoo.

Over the wild green jungles he flew. Snatched at by monkeys and screamed at by baboons.

At last he got out of the jungles by the strength of his brave white wings.

And soon he was over the wild still
wastes of the Sahara Desert.
Then suddenly the silence of the sand
was broken by an onrush of wings.
There were the other storks returning to
the land of their birth.
And he flew with them over the desert
towards the cool Northern spring.

Then one day in early spring there was
    the gentle rustle of birds building a
    nest of straw and twigs on top of
    the chimney.
The farmer had been expecting them.
He had tied a wheel on his chimney.
He knew storks are a sign of good luck
    to any house on which they choose
    to build.

First there were two

And then

Spring had come

And the story starts all over again.